We Love CHRISTMAS JUMBO COLORING BOOK

Published by Playmore Inc. Publishers, 58 Main Street, 2nd Floor, Hackensack, N.J. 07601
and Waldman Publishing Corp., 570 Seventh Avenue, New York, N.Y. 10018

Printed in Canada

Santa invites Mary and Peter to join him...

... on his Christmas visit to the zoo.

Santa uses his special key to open the zoo gate.

Santa's magical dream dust makes the guards fall fast asleep.

The huge elephant carries Santa through the zoo.

All the animals are happy to see him.

Peter, Mary, and the animals watch as Santa waves his hands...

... and suddenly, a beautifully decorated Christmas tree appears!

With another magical wave of his hands ...

... Santa makes all the cages disappear!

DRAWING LESSON

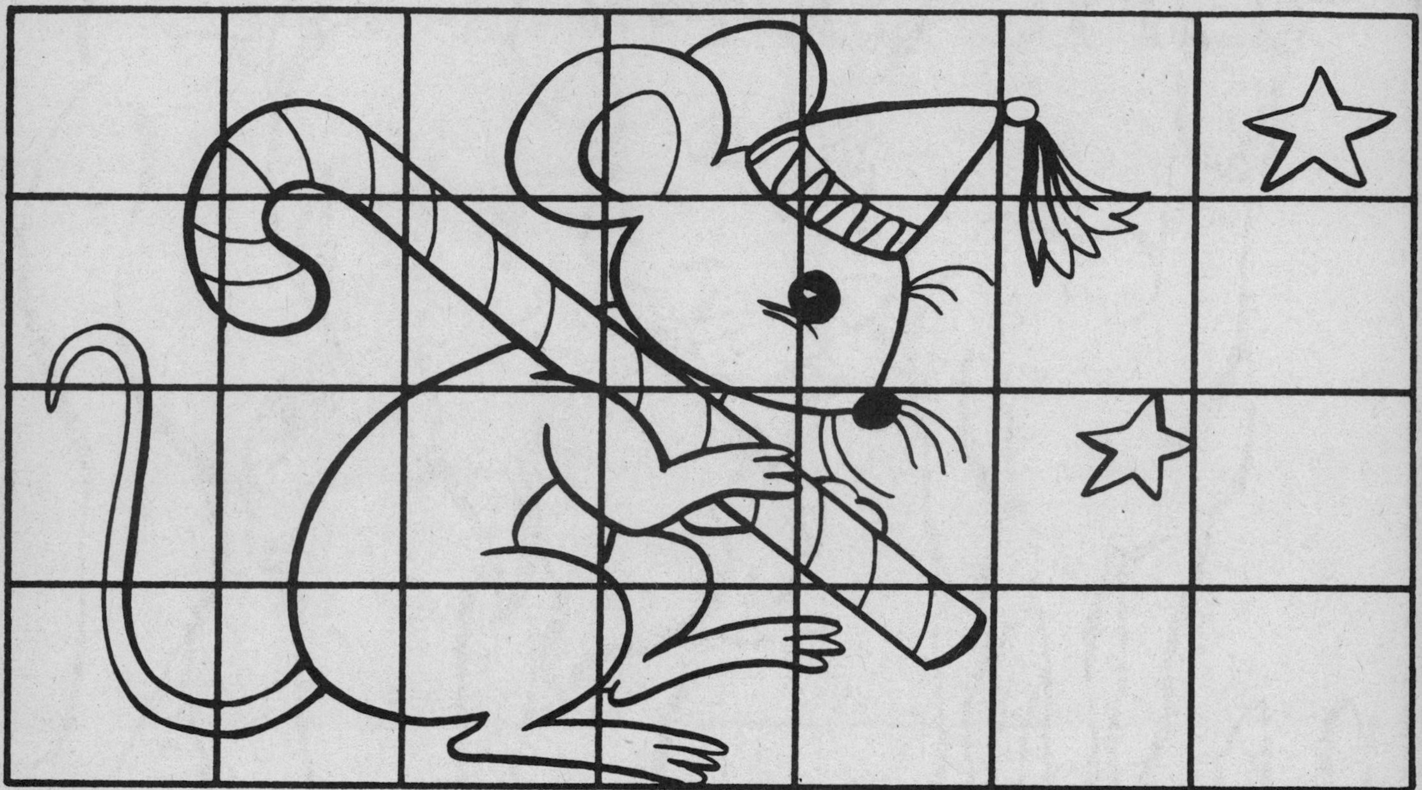

DRAW A MOUSE IN THE SQUARES BELOW.

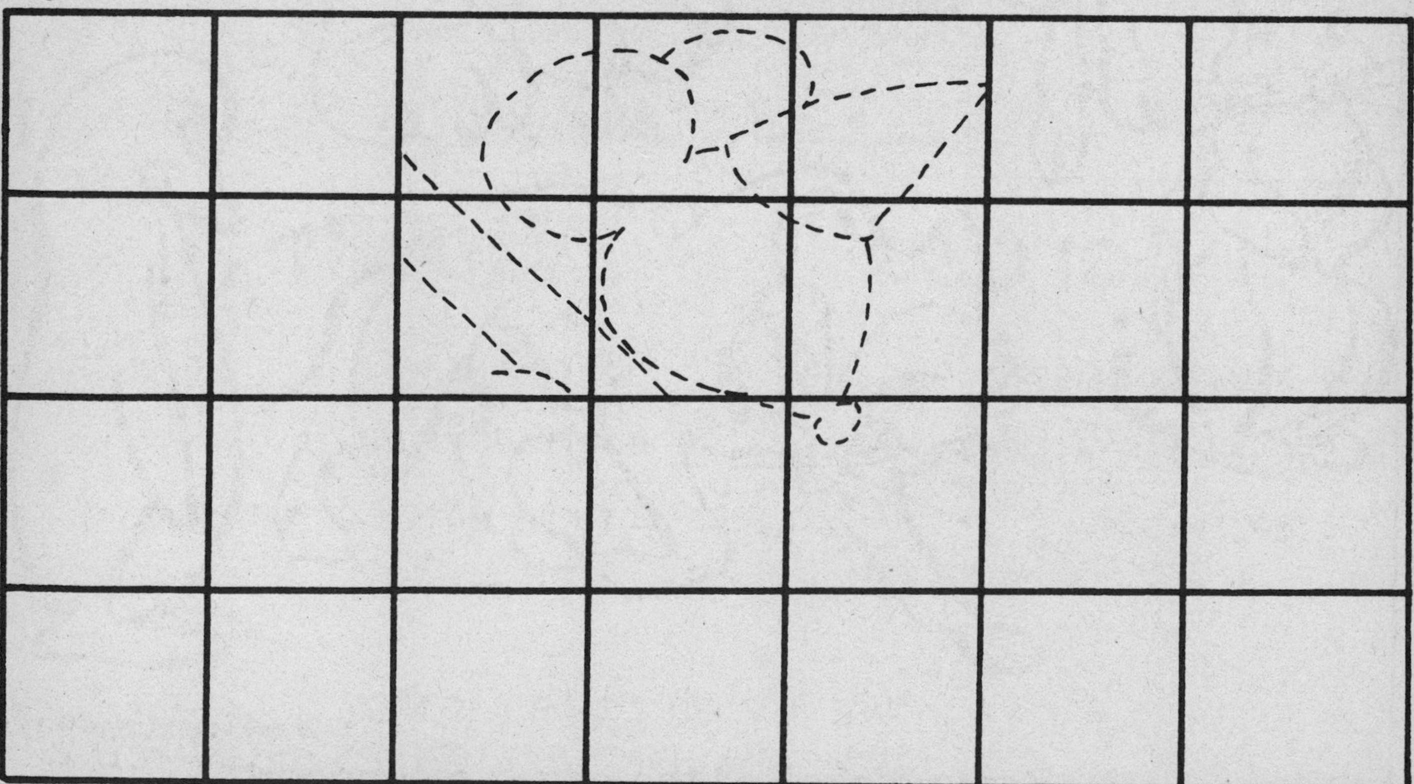

DROPPING IN

Across

2. SANTA'S LAUGH
3. WHAT SANTA COMES DOWN
5. NOT NIGHT

Down

1. NOT A GIRL
2. ASSIST OR AID
4. FIFTH MONTH OF THE YEAR

ANSWERS: ACROSS: 2.HO 3.CHIMNEY 5.DAY
DOWN: 1.BOY 2.HELP 4.MAY

Leo Lion and Lana Lamb play together as friends.

Even Mortimer Mouse and Calvin Cat exchange gifts.

"A ride on the zoo train is fu-u-u-n!"
says Elmer Elephant ...

... as Melvin Monkey drives them
round and round the zoo.

Mary and Peter join the animal at the zoo's ice skating pond.

Harry Hippo is out in front,
with Ricky Robin close behind.

The animals love tobogganing too.

"Hold on at the rear, Petey Pelican!"

All the animals love to ride the zoo merry-go-round.

Round and round and round they go and go and go!

Mary lights the big Christmas candle.

“We’re all invited to the animals’ Christmas costume party,” says Santa.

Melvin Monkey, dressed as a jester, plays his banjo for Maxwell Moose.

“Good health to all!” toasts Sir Zachary Zebra
to Lady Priscilla Penguin.

Find the twin pelicans.

Answer: 2 and 4

COLOR BY NUMBER:
The Best Christmas Presents Ever!
1-orange 2-green 3-pink 4-brown 5-red 6-blue

The animals gather colorful balloons
for the Christmas party.

“I have three balloons,”
says Roger Raccoon to Felicia Fawn.

Santa plays the violin for the guests ...

... while Lori and Lisa Leopard sing a Christmas carol.

Percy Parrot and Stanley Stork exchange gifts ...

... with Conrad Camel.

Mary holds the royal robe of Leora, Queen of Lions ...

... while Peter does the same for Leo, King of Lions.

Gerald Giraffe loves his gigantic necktie.

Terry Tiger enjoys pretending he is the Prince of India.

The Koala family watch the Christmas show from a tree.

And Jimmy Jackal does a great job
as the mean Mr. Scrooge!

FOLLOW THE DOTS and see who is happy with his Christmas toothbrush.

COLOR BY NUMBER:
A Gift That's Good Enough to Eat!

1-white 2-black 3-orange 4-brown 5-red 6-blue

Take Calvin Caribou to Mortimer Mouse
so they can turn on the Christmas lights.

How many hidden turtles can you find
in the koala picture?

Answer: 7

Sammy Seal plays a Christmas song on his horns ...

What fun to see Kenny and Kerry Kangaroo
dance and jump!

... while Rita Rhino does a graceful ballet dance.

Wally Wart Hog plays a Christmas song on his tuba.

Billy, Buddy, and Barney Bear formed a band ...

... so they could play and sing at the Christmas party.

Timothy Turtle arrives with a small Christmas tree on his back.

Calvin Caribou has his own built-in Christmas tree!

Charlie Chimpanzee juggles five different objects ...

... and his brother, Chester, does a balancing act on a wheel.

“Hooray! The trick worked!”

“Speak no evil, hear no evil, see no evil,”
say the three monkeys.

Warren Wolf and his family howl their Christmas carols.

"Jungle bells! Jungle bells! Jungle all the way ...."

Percy Polar Bear reads a Christmas story to
Patrick Penguin.

Waldo Walrus listens as he smokes his pipe.

And Busy Benny Beaver takes a rest as he listens.

Oliver Opossum watches television in his tree.

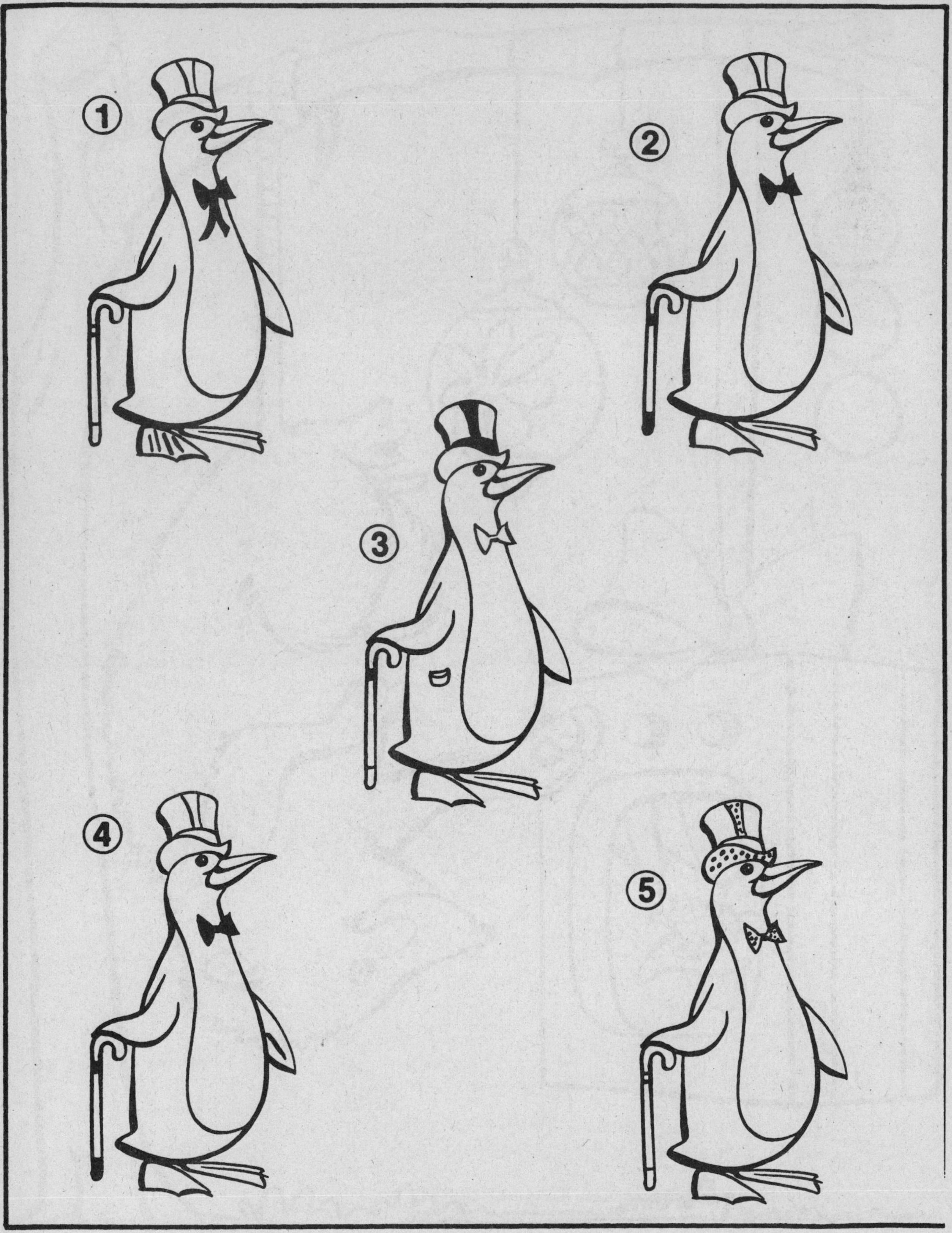

Find Patrick and Penrod -
the twin penguins at the party.

Answer: 2 and 4

Find 5 mistakes in this orchestra picture.

Answers: Bubbles are coming out of the saxaphone; the owl has two different ears; the hippo has a keyhole in his belt; the cat has three eyes; one of the cat's drum is a bucket.

And here's the greatest Christmas treat of all —

the Animal Zoo Orchestra playing dance music!

Olivia Owl dances with Freddie Fox,
Melissa Mouse with Timothy Turtle ...

... and Elmer Elephant spins around the floor
with Ginger Giraffe.

Mary enjoys dancing with Petey Pelican.

The party ends with Maryann Moose gaily dancing with Santa.

All the animals thank Santa for a wonderful party.

“Ho! Ho! Ho!” says Santa. “I had a wonderful time too!”

"A very Merry Christmas to you all!"

Find 5 mistakes in this dancing picture.

Answers: The pelican is wearing one sneaker; Mary has on two different boots; the pelican is wearing two ties; the umbrella handle is a candy cane; Mary has six fingers on her right hand.

Help Randy Rabbit pop out of Freddie Fox's magic hat.

DRAWING LESSON

Draw Leo Lion and his Christmas ornament
in the boxes below.

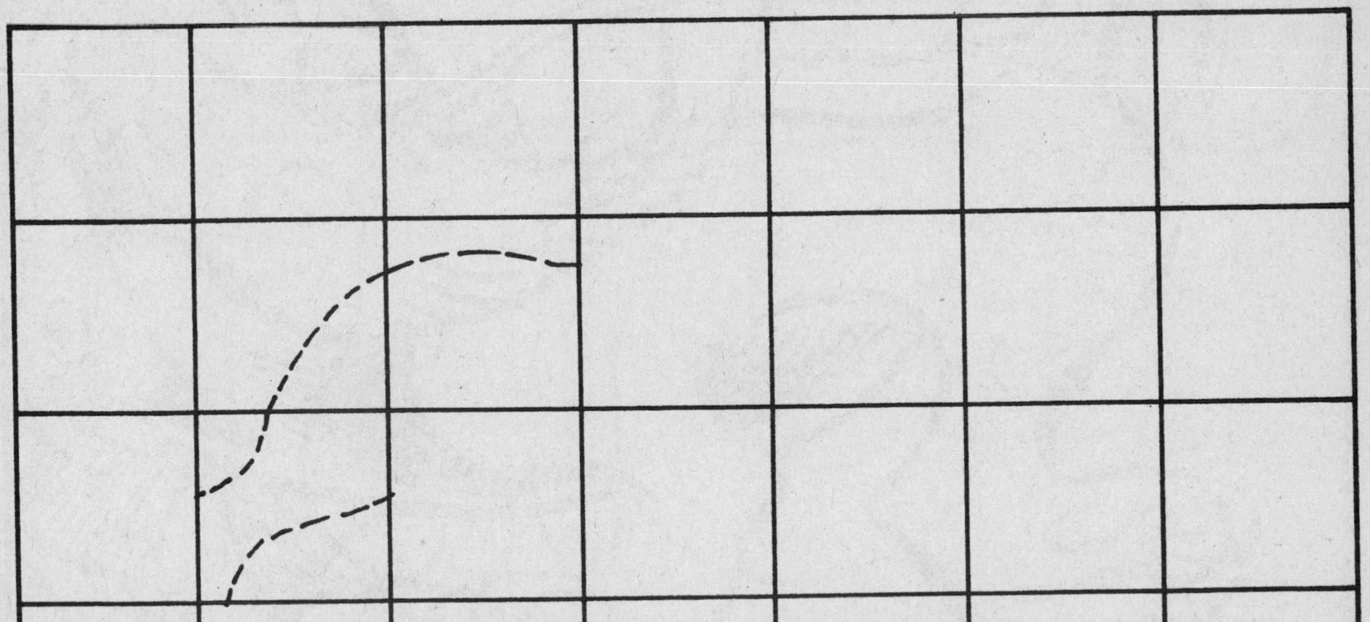

HIDDEN PICTURES:
Can you find a pencil, a fish, a bottle,
a top, a spoon, and a heart?

Help Melvin Monkey gather enough snowballs
to build his snowman.

Christmas Bear's Christmas Eve

It's Christmas Eve, and Christmas Bear puts milk and cookies out for Santa.

The only thing left to do is put the star
on top of the tree.

Christmas Bear stands on tiptoe ...

... but the tree begins to fall!

Christmas Bear holds the tree up, but he's stuck.
If he lets the tree go, it will tumble to the floor.

Christmas Bear needs help!

Just when Christmas Bear is about to let go,
he hears a merry "Ho, ho, ho."

Santa helps Christmas Bear save the tree. "I think you need a treat, Christmas Bear," Santa says.

Merry Christmas, Santa.
Merry Christmas, Christmas Bear.

MATCH THE SHADOW

ONLY ONE OF THE FIVE GIRLS MATCHES THE SHADOW. WHICH ONE IS IT?

1

2

3

4

5

ANSWER : 5

How many scrambled balloons
is Roger Raccoon carrying?

Answer: 14

FOLLOW THE DOTS and see who is wearing his Christmas boxing gloves.

COLOR BY NUMBER:
A Handy Carry-All for Christmas Goodies!

1-white 2-orange 3-red 4-brown 5-yellow 6-blue

Find the twin Santa hippos at the party.

Answer: 3 ans 4

DRAWING LESSON

Draw Melvin Monkey in the boxes below.

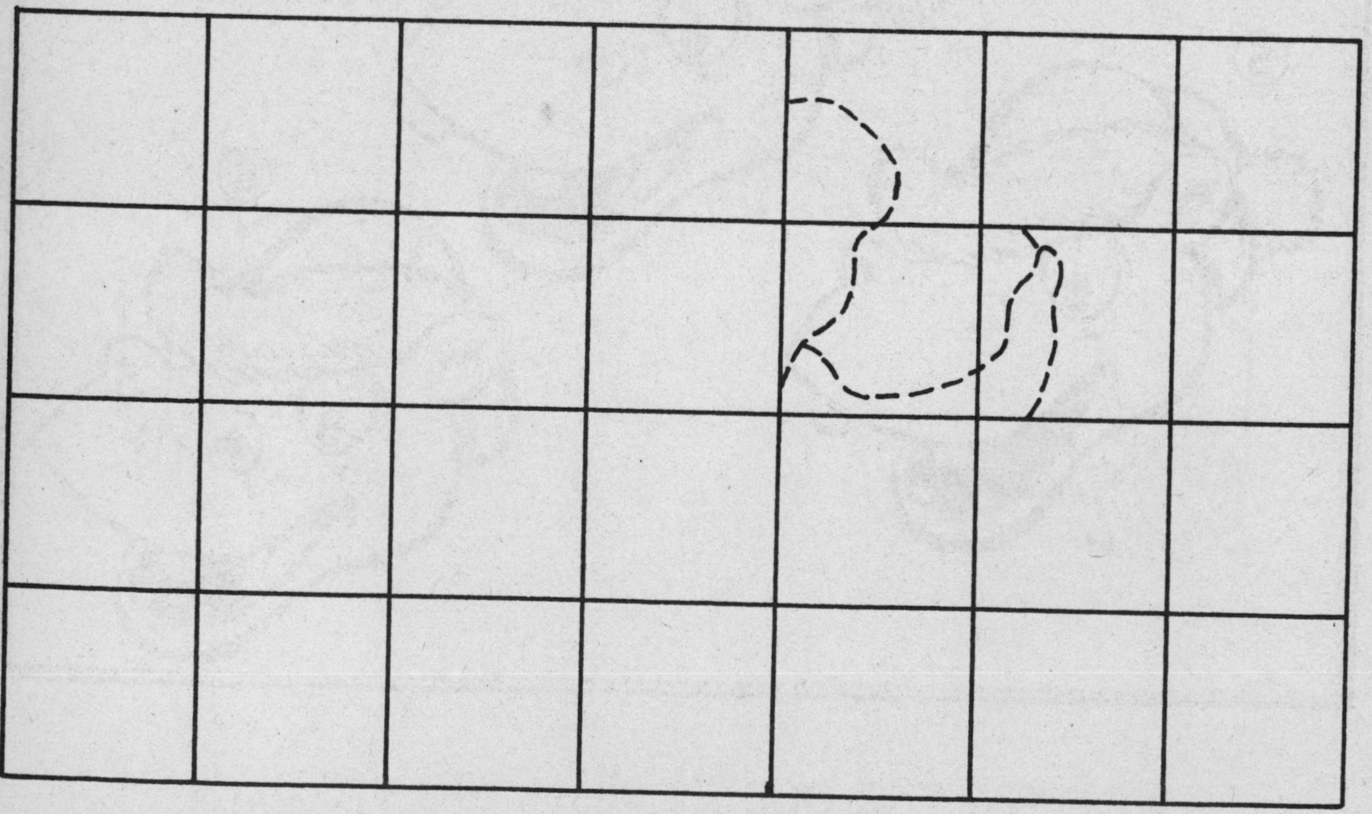

FOLLOW THE DOTS and see who is doing a
Christmas balancing trick.

Christmas is a time of joy and love around the world.

Store windows hold shining displays of toys and gifts.

In many countries
peoples send Christmas cards and gifts.

What fun to wrap them in bright paper
and colorful ribbons!

People in Poland bake small wafers called *oplatki*. They exchange *oplatki* just as other people exchange Christmas cards.

People in Italy give out their Christmas gifts
from a large clay jar called "The Urn of Fate".

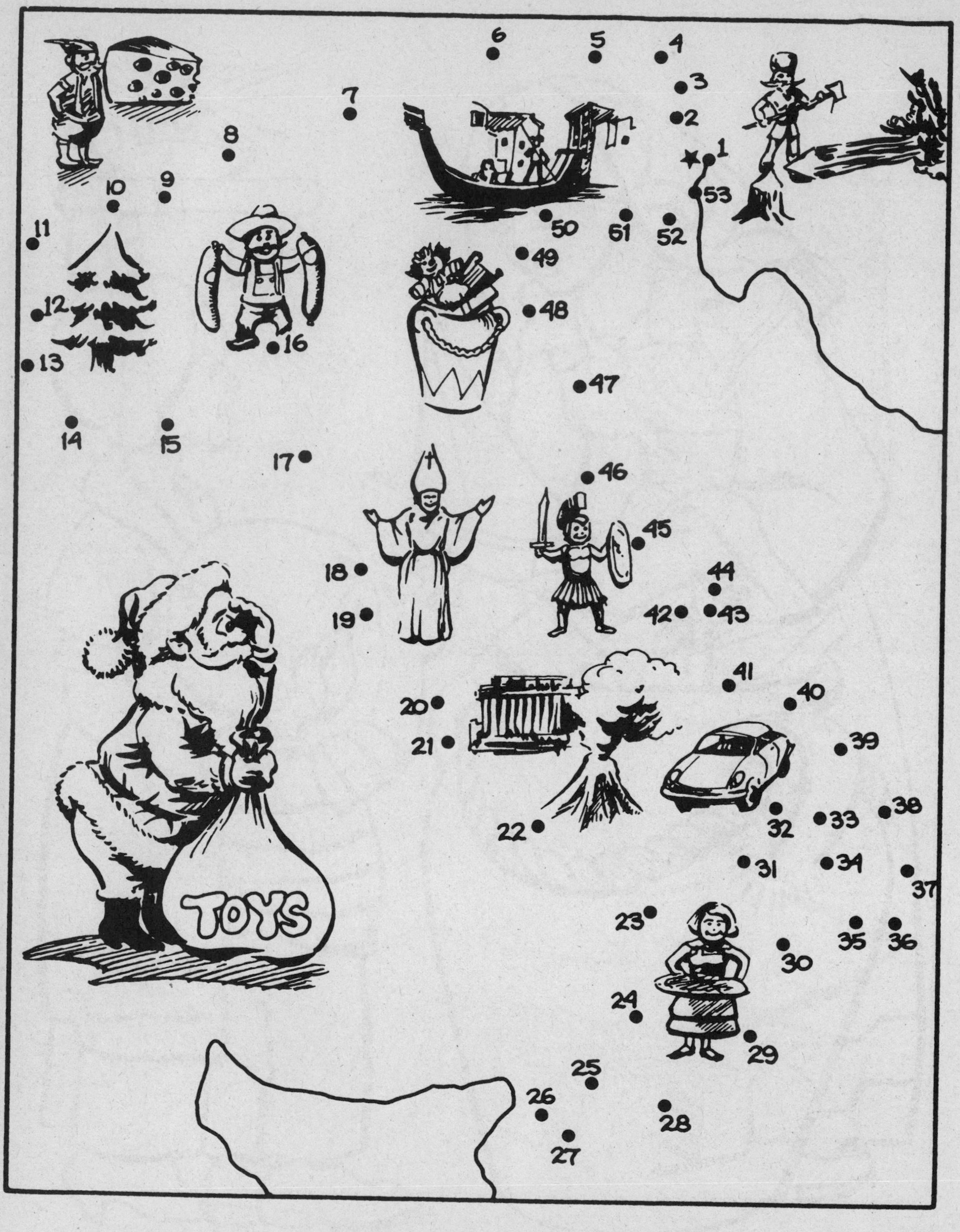

FOLLOW THE DOTS and help Santa find out what country he is in.

Help Mortimer Mouse put the star at the top of his Christmas tree.

COLOR BY NUMBER:

"I can help Santa give out the zoo gifts."

1-brown 2-orange 3-red 4-green 5-yellow 6-white

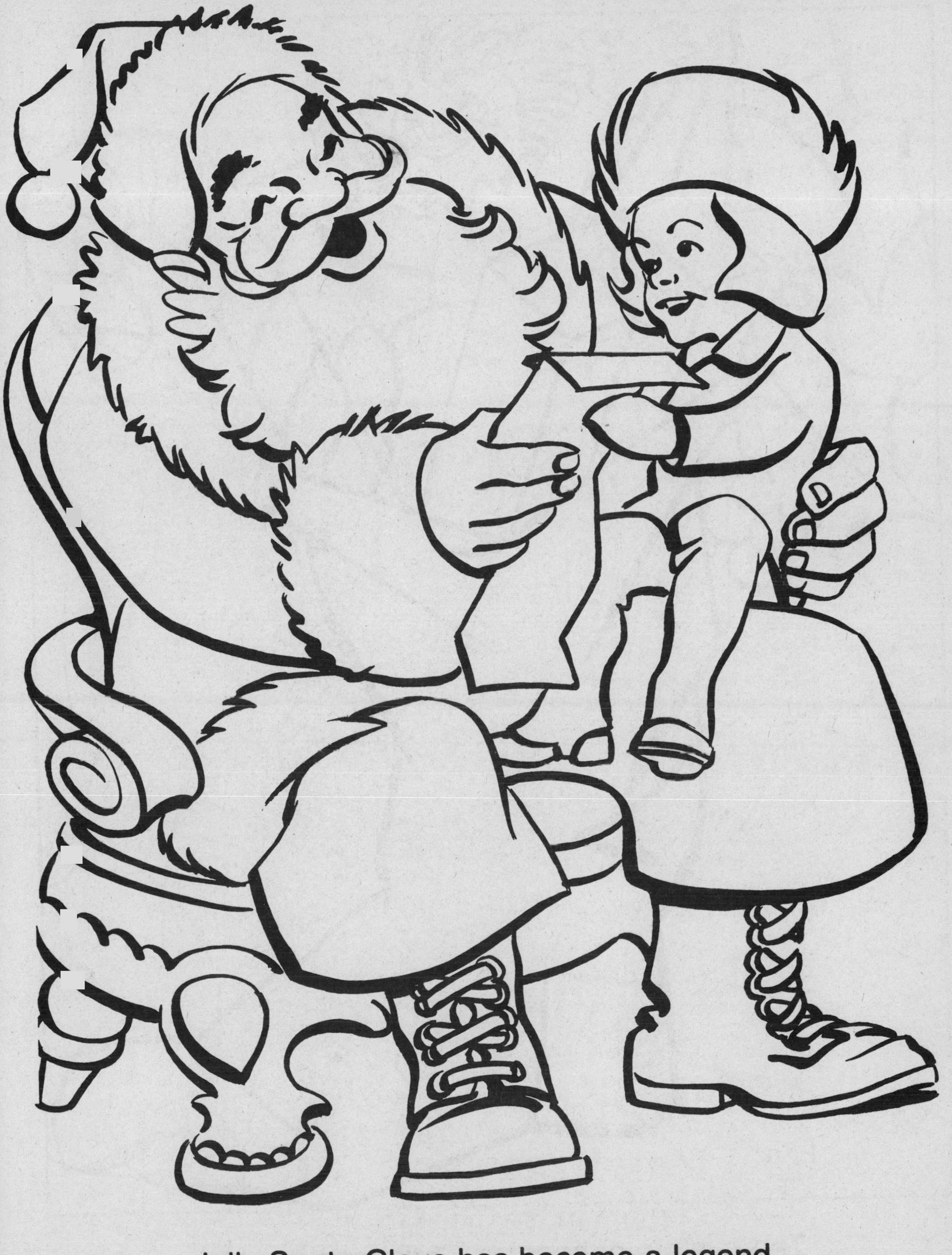

Jolly Santa Claus has become a legend
in the United States.

The custom of hanging Christmas stockings began in England.

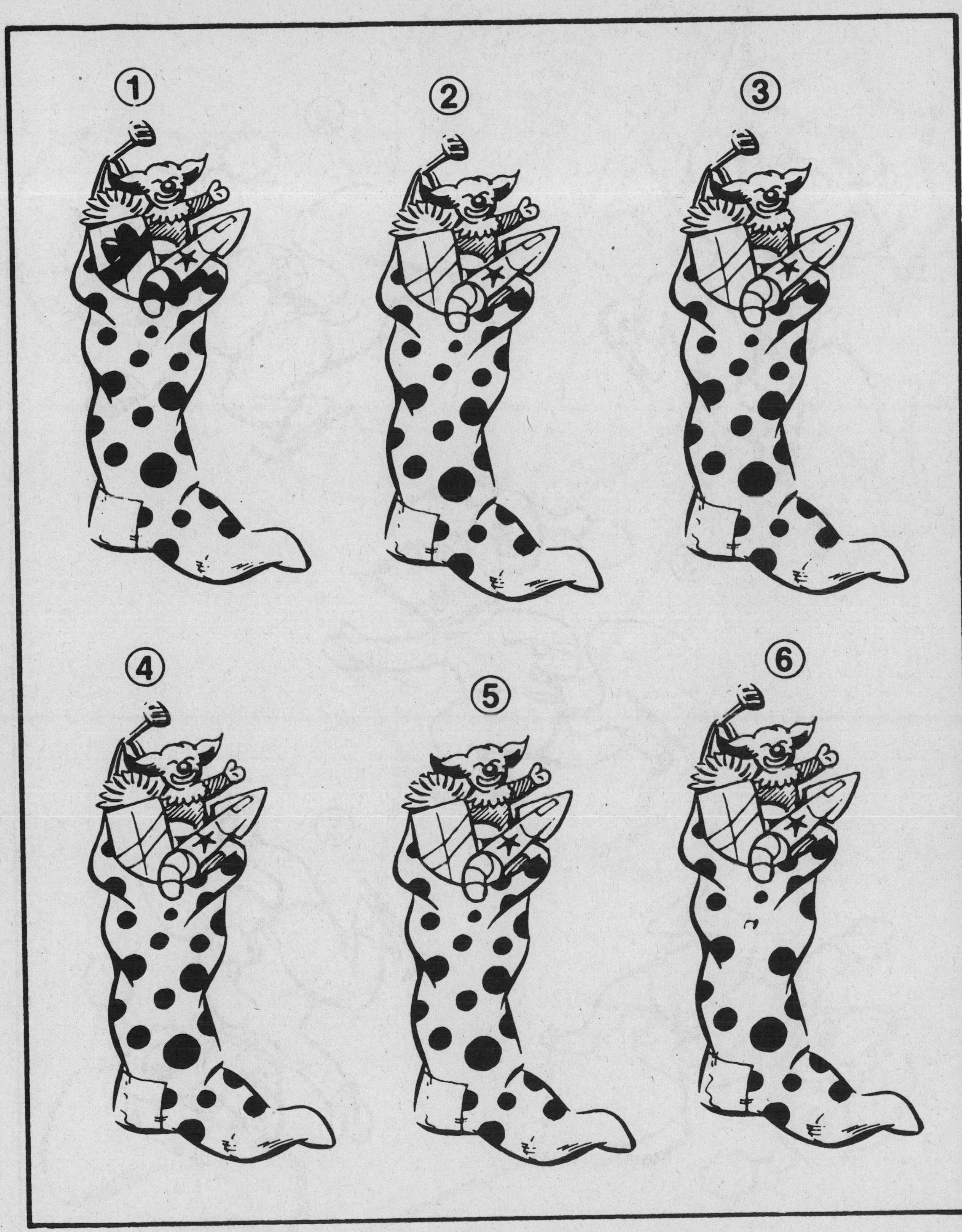

Find the twin Christmas stockings.

Answer: 2 and 4

Find Melvin and Marvin Mouse –
the skating twins at the zoo.

Answer: 3 and 5

Which skater will win the race to the finish line?

In towns in every land, the streets are busy places.

The town Christmas tree sparkles with decorations.

Children everywhere gather in their homes ...

... to hear the story of the first Christmas.

With its green leaves and red berries, holly makes gay Christmas wreaths for doors and windows.

Today, standing under the mistletoe means you'll get kissed!

Candles in many shapes and sizes add a festive air
to Christmas ...

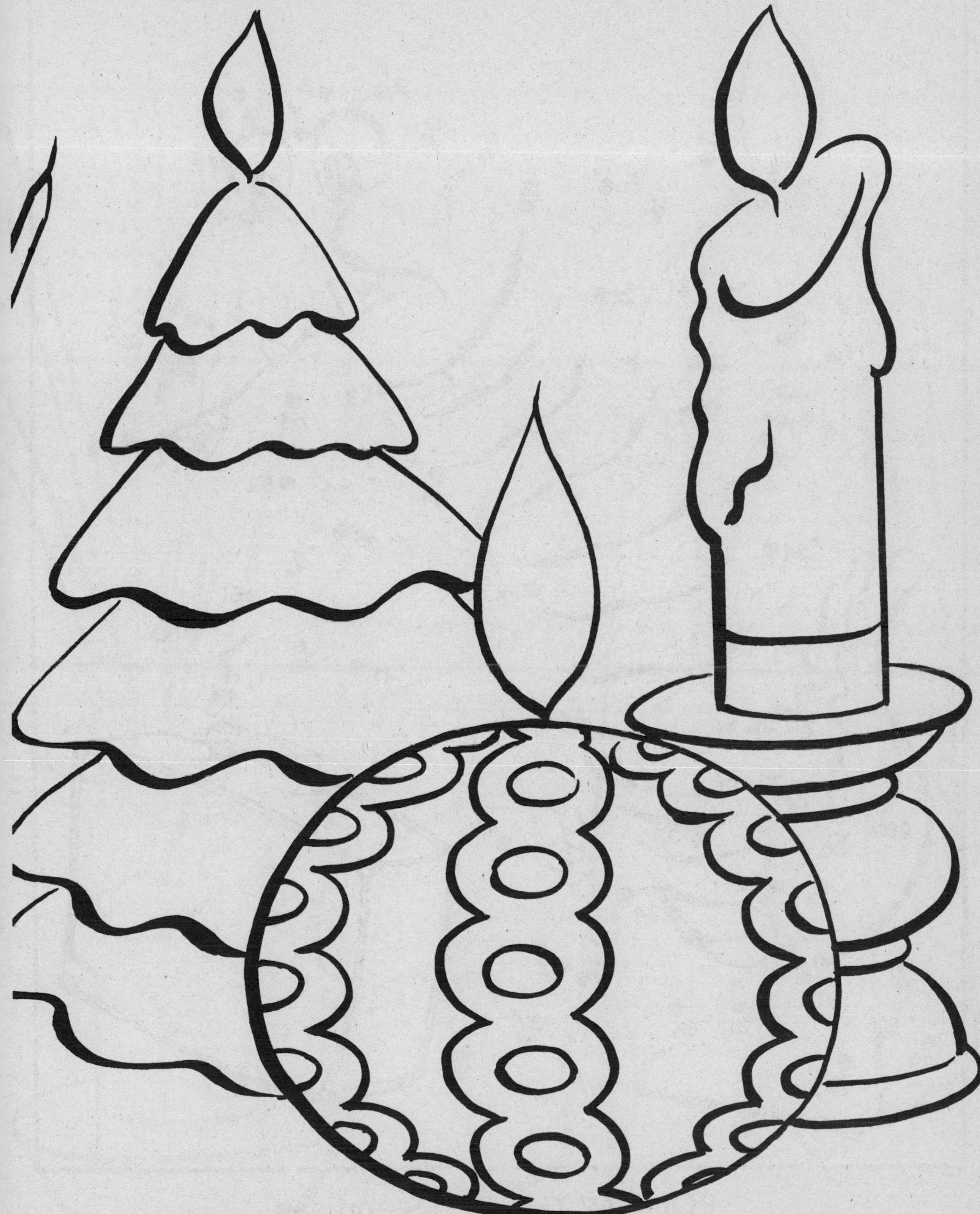

... and are a part of religious services in churches throughout the world.

FOLLOW THE DOTS and see who is going on a trip with his Christmas suitcase.

Who will win the downhill snow race?

How many of Terry Tiger's hidden milk bottles can you find?

Answer: 11

Find the twin crocodiles.

Answer: 2 and 5

For nine nights before Christmas, Mexican children act out *La Posada* – the story of Mary and Joseph's search for rooms on the first Christmas.

The children go from house to house and beg to enter.
But they are refused ... until they reach the door
to the stable.

Holly branches have been part of Christmas decorations for many years.

Long ago, Christmas guests traveled by sled.

People in many states still follow Christmas customs brought to America by early settlers.

Musicians went from house to house and were treated to hot drinks and cakes.

Santa is almost finished with his work.

His eight reindeer are ready to head home.

Find 6 mistakes in the zoo-keeper's picture.

Answers: Santa has a patch in his beard; the fireplace is in the desk; the telephone is on the side of the desk; the zoo-keeper's sign is upside-down; the zoo-keeper's toes stick out of his shoe; Santa has only one eyebrow.

FOLLOW THE DOTS and see who is wearing his new cowboy boots to the party.

Help Ricky Robin find his way down Santa Snowman
to reach Timothy Turtle.

Because the ground in the Scandinavian countries
is covered with snow, children feed the birds
at Christmas time.

In Sweden, Christmas begins with the Fesival of Lights
on St. Lucia's Day, December 13.

Fill in the names of the animals going across in the ZOO CROSSWORD. Then read the mystery person for 1 down.

Answers: 1-seal, 2-walrus, 3-monkey, 4-tiger, 5-bear, 6-cat, 7-wolf, 8-beaver, 9-turtle, 10-moose.
Mystery Person: Santa Claus

The custom of cutting and burning a Yule log is
an ancient one.

In many countries, it is still part of the Christmas celebration.

In Mexico, a gaily decorated *piñata* is hung from a tree.

Break the *piñata* with a stick
and out will come candy and gifts for everyone!

French Canadian children feed their cats well on December 24 . . .

. . . for it's bad luck if a cat meows on Christmas Eve.

In Yugoslavia, woodcutters chop a tree at sunrise.
If it falls to the East, it means good luck.

In Czechoslovakia, if a girl puts a twig in water on December 4 and it blooms before Christmas Eve, she will marry that year.

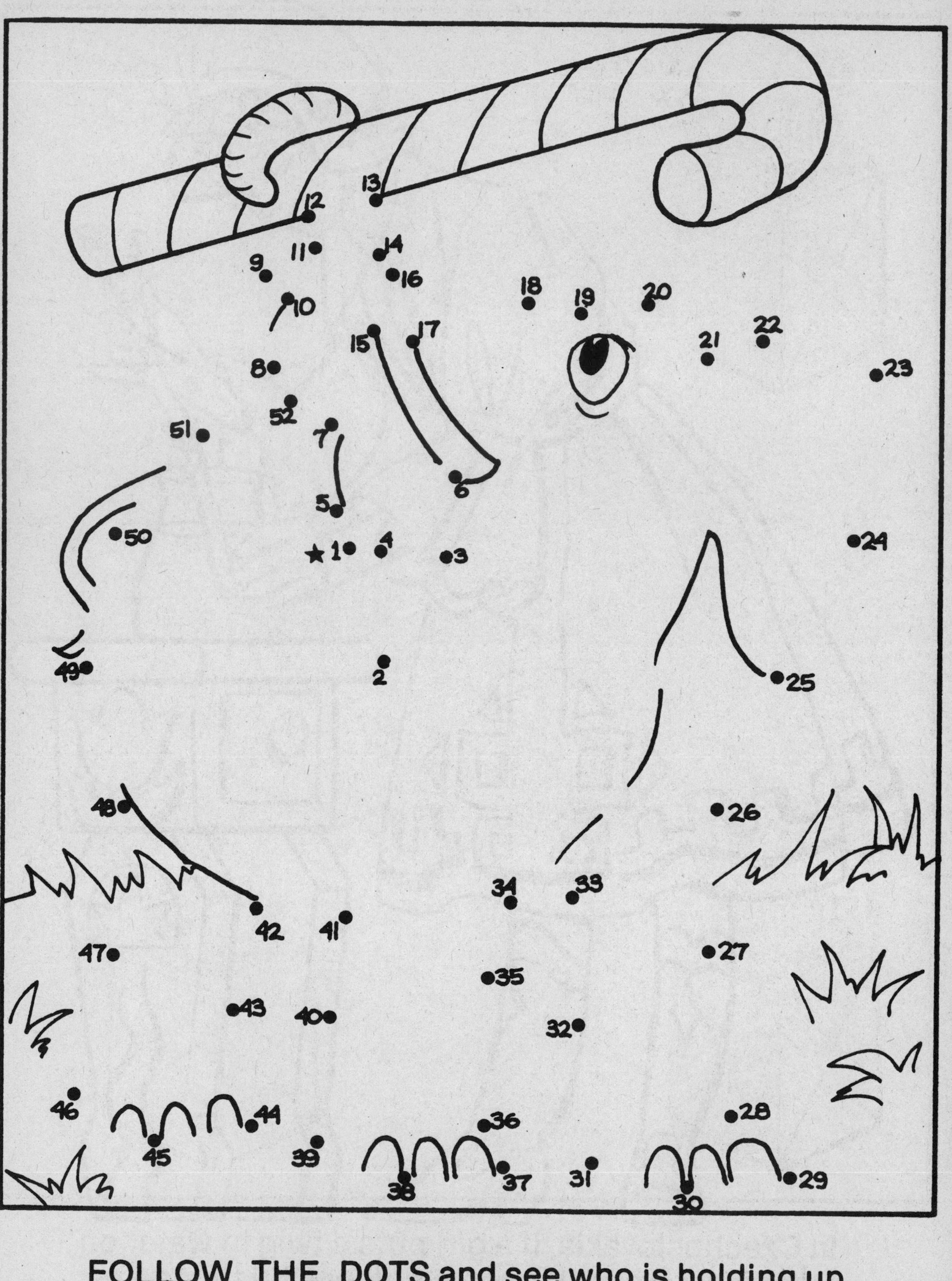

FOLLOW THE DOTS and see who is holding up a giant candy cane.

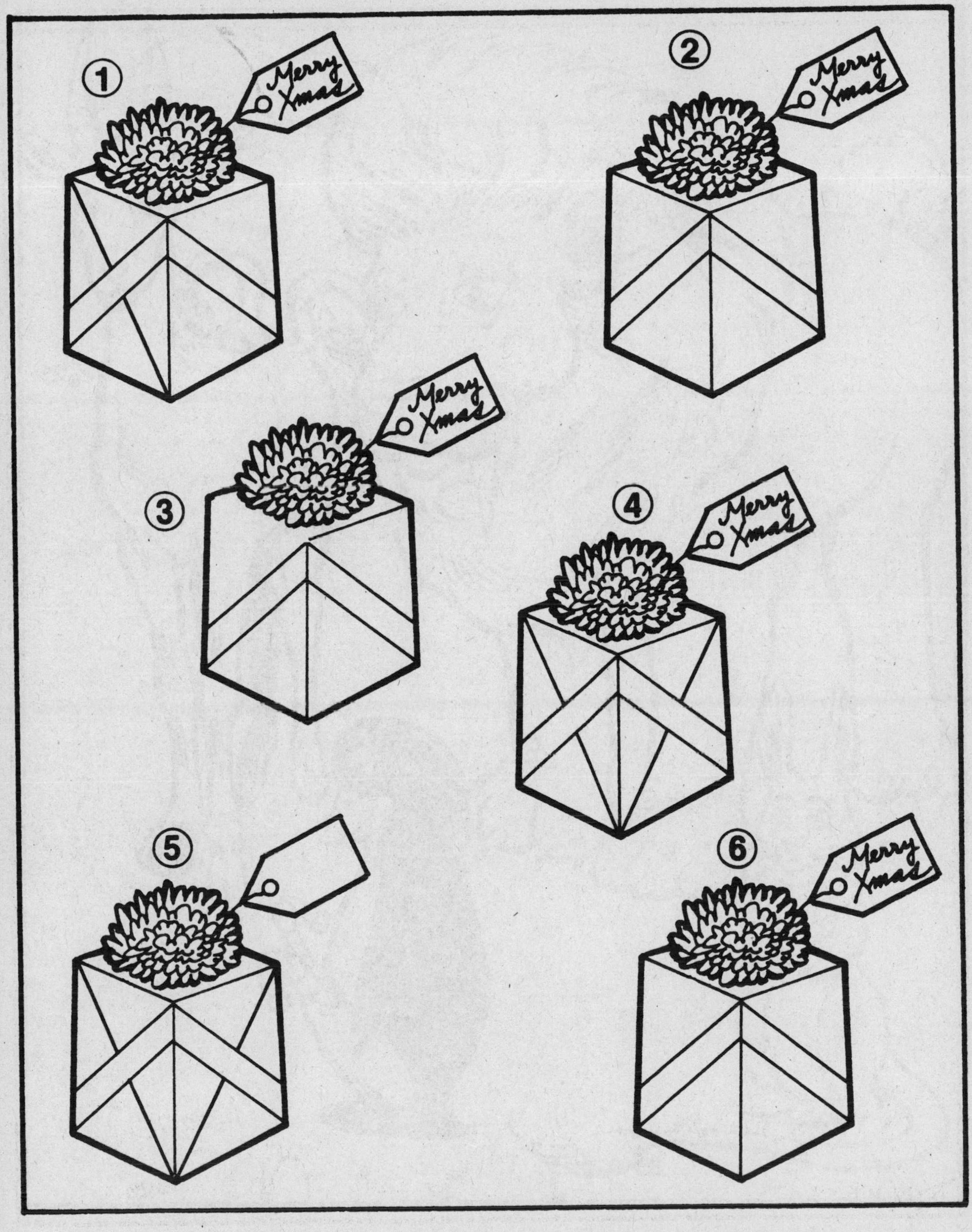

Find the twin gifts Santa will take to the zoo.

Answer: 2 and 6

Find 6 mistakes in the animals waiting for their gifts.

Answers: The lion has a rabbit's tail; the rabbit has a lion's tail; the lion has fangs; the antelope has one horse's hoof; the antelope has two tails; the penguin has a pouch.

Help Santa land near the gate to the zoo.

DRAWING LESSON

Draw this Swedish Candle-Boy in the boxes at the right.

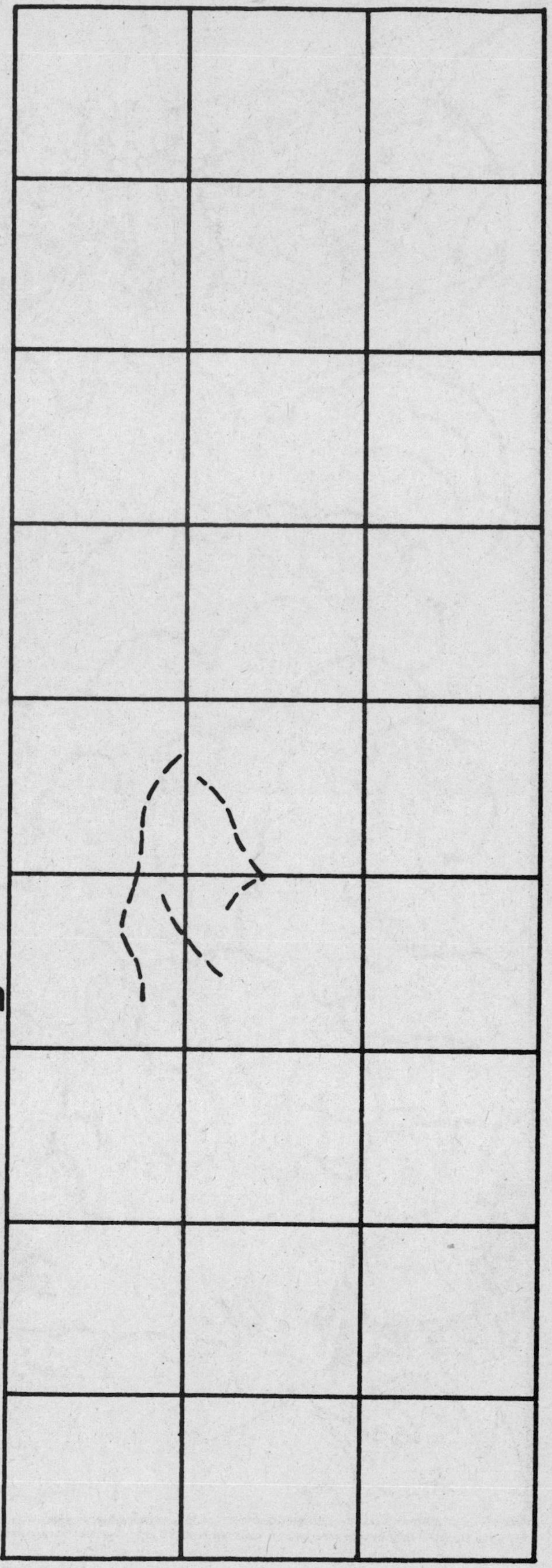

COLOR BY NUMBER: "Break the *piñata*, not my head!"
1-pink 2-green 3-brown 4-yellow 5-red 6-orange

Mistletoe was first used by ancient priests
in their religious ceremonies.

King Henry VII introduced the wassail bowl to England.
The bowl contains hot ale, spices, and toasted apples.

In Scotland, oatmeal cookies, called bannock cakes, are served.

In Ireland,
a candle burns in every window on Christmas Eve.

Plum pudding began in England. It is made with raisins, dried citrus fruits, beef fat, sugar, and spices.

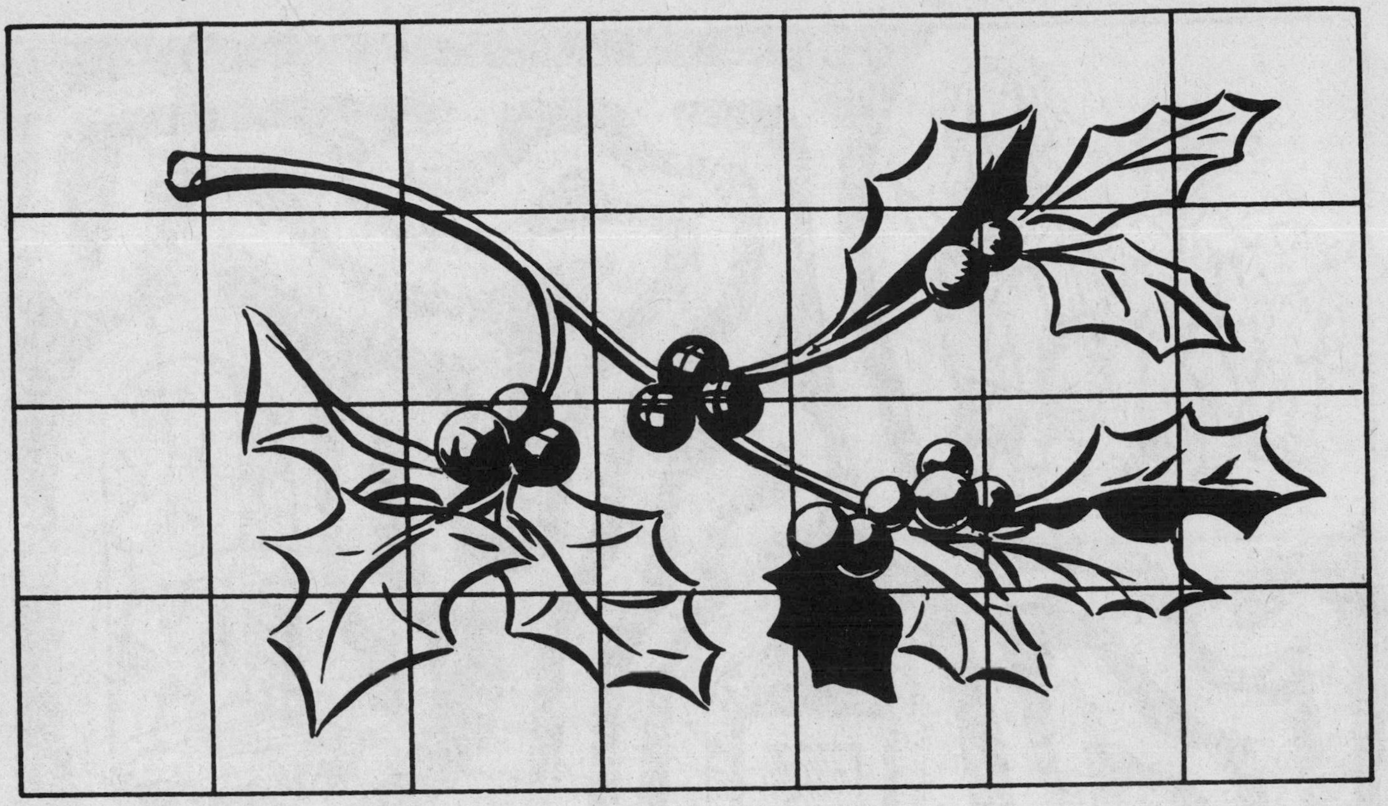

DRAWING LESSON

Draw the holly branch in the boxes below.

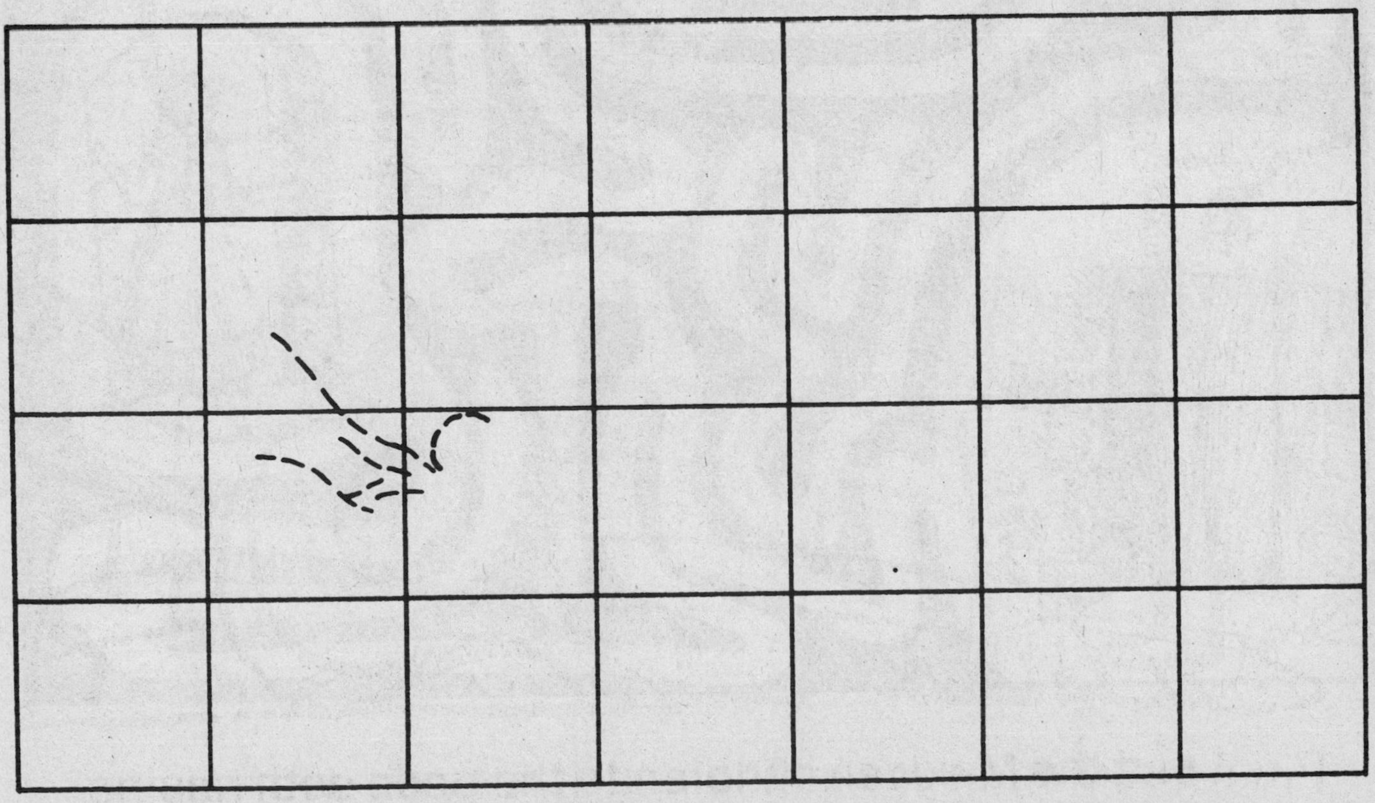

Lead the Mexican children to the open doorway
as they act out *La Posada.*

Find the twin urns filled with gifts.

Answer: 1 and 4

How many hidden elves can you find?

Answer: 6

December 26 — Boxing Day in England — is the time when gifts are given to servants and tradesmen.

In Denmark and Sweden, Christmas elves,
called *Júúl Nisse*, are said to help with chores . . .

. . . but Júúl Nisse also cause trouble!

In Sweden, burning candles surround a straw goat.
The goat is ready to butt any bad children
during the Christmas season.

In Finland, villagers lay a carpet of green pine branches from a hilltop to the center of their village.

The Beacon Hill Bell-Ringers of Boston, Massachusetts . . .

. . . sound out Christmas carols on their hand bells.

DRAWING LESSON

Draw this Mexican *piñata* in the boxes below.

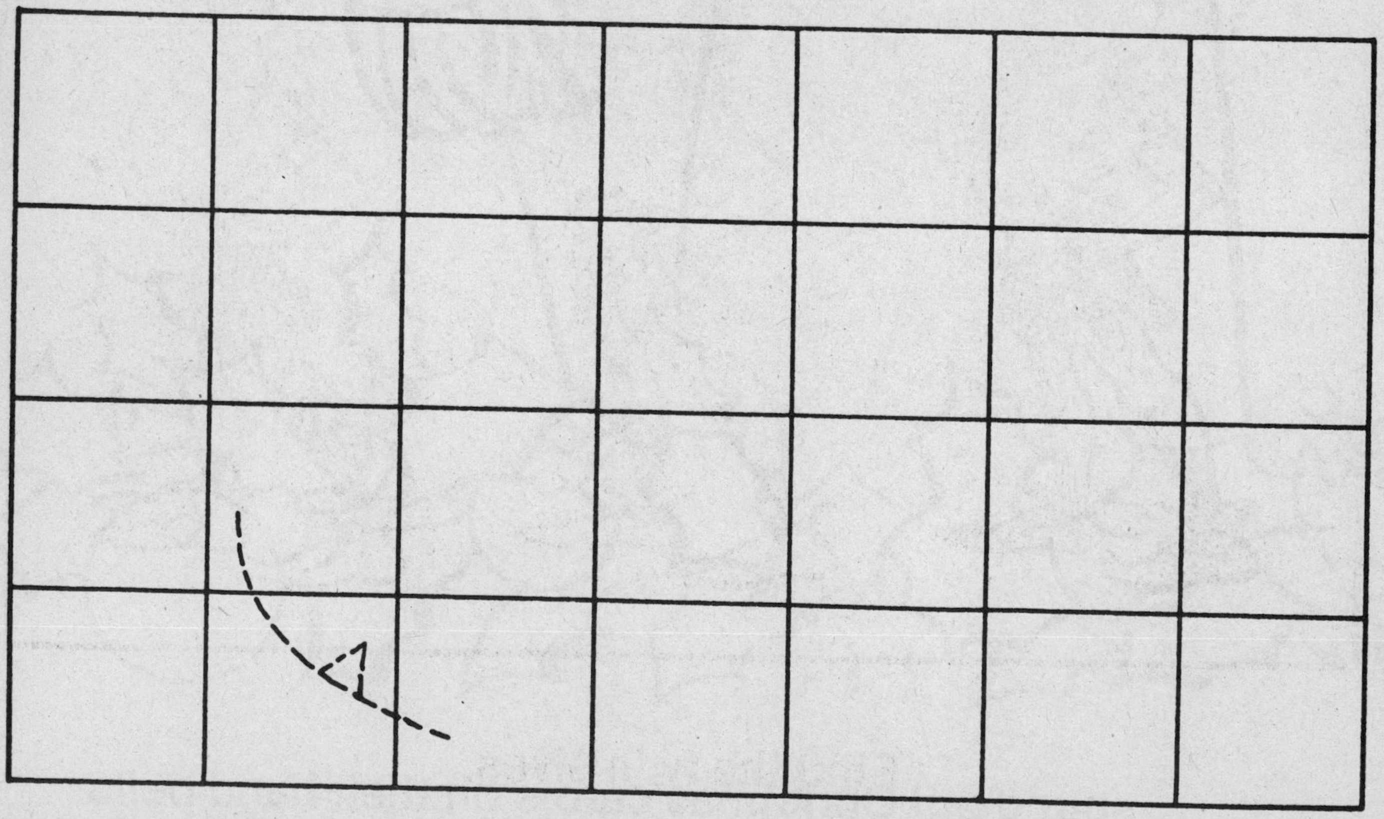

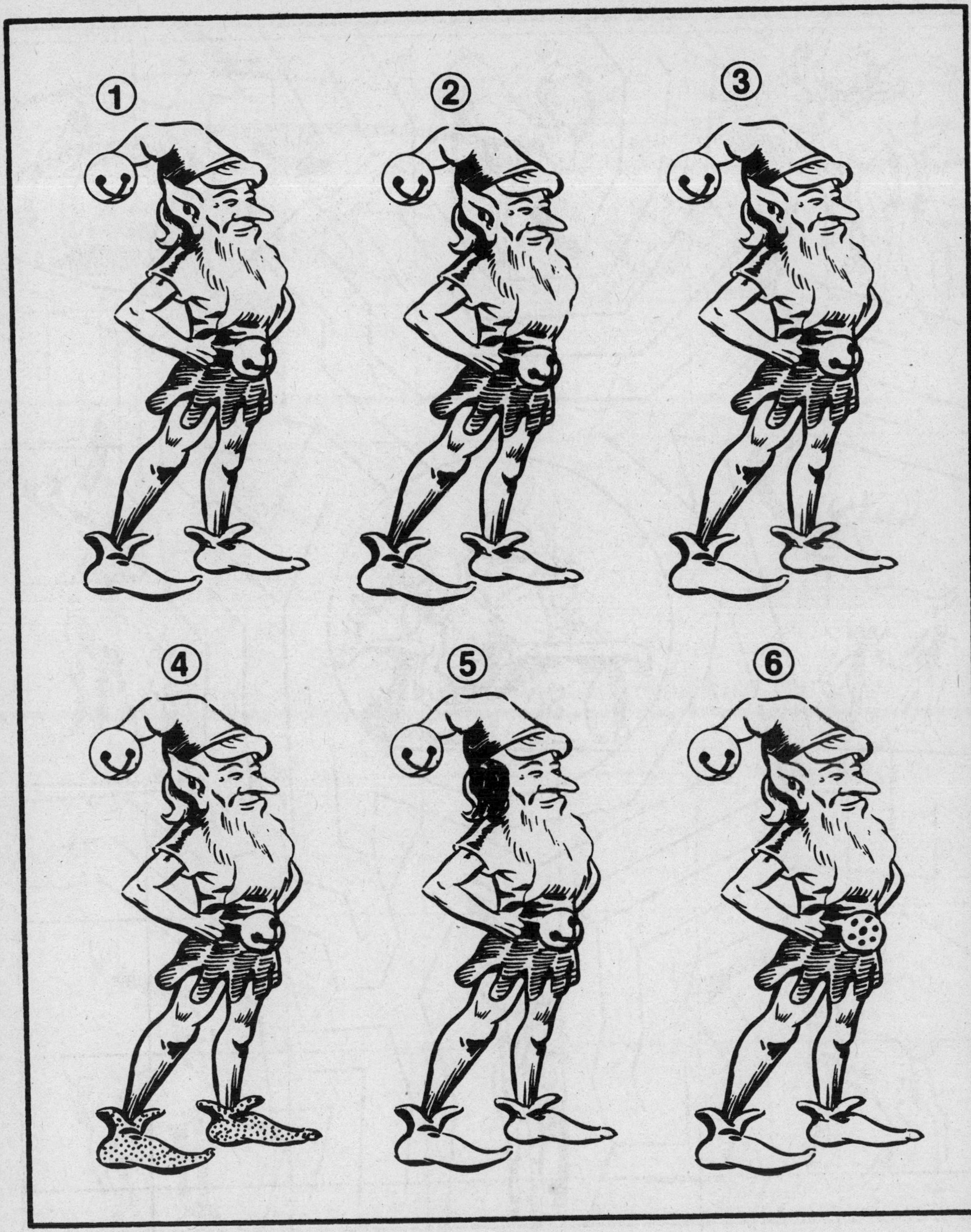

Find the twin elves.

Answer: 1 and 3

Lead ALL 8 reindeer to Santa's sleigh.

COLOR BY NUMBER: Who's butting in?

1-yellow 2-red 3-pink 4-green 5-light blue 6-orange

Chrildren in Belgium, Luxembourg, and The Netherlands receive gifts from Saint Nicholas on his feast day, December 6.

Christian children in China and Japan celebrate Christmas much like American children — with songs and plays.

Years ago in Russia, a beautiful girl in a sleigh
was drawn through the snowy streets.

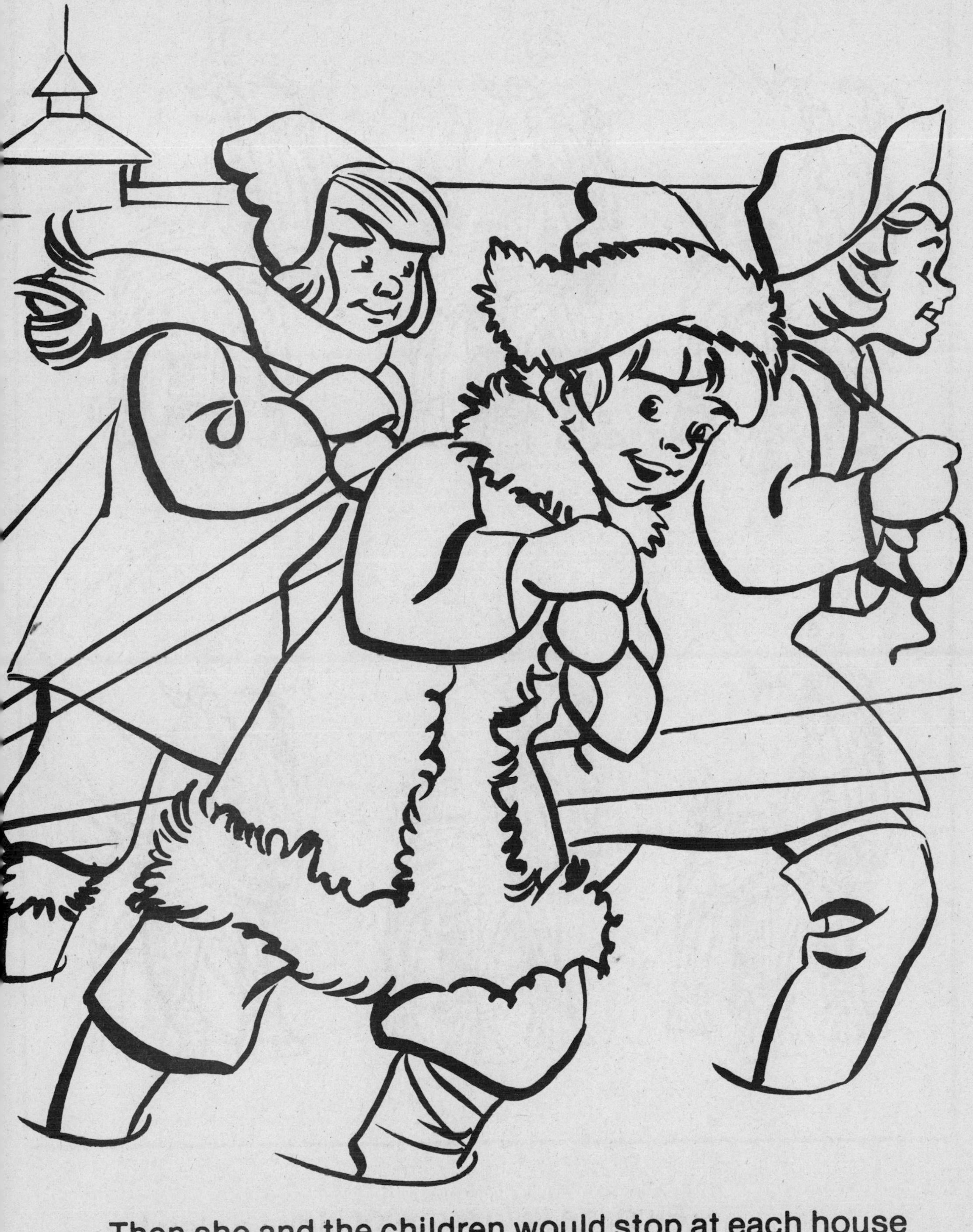

Then she and the children would stop at each house
to sing to the townspeople.

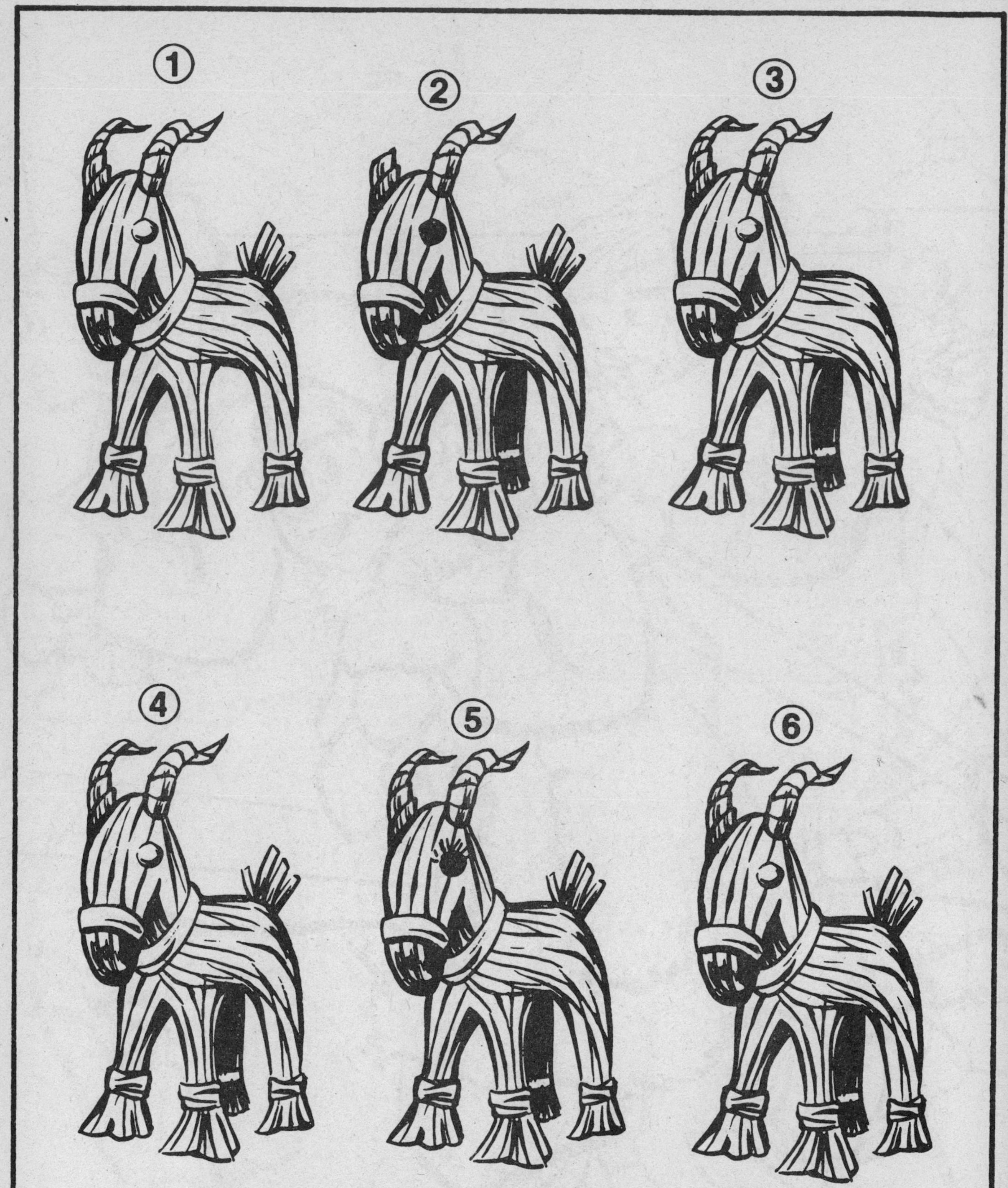

Find the twin straw goats.

Answer: 4 and 6

The star is used everywhere as a Christmas symbol.
In the Ukraine, a star-bearer walks with the carolers.

COLOR BY NUMBER:

What is this Czech girl doing at Christmas?

1-light blue 2-white 3-yellow 4-red 5-purple 6-pink

DRAWING LESSON

Draw King Henry's wassail bowl in the boxes below.

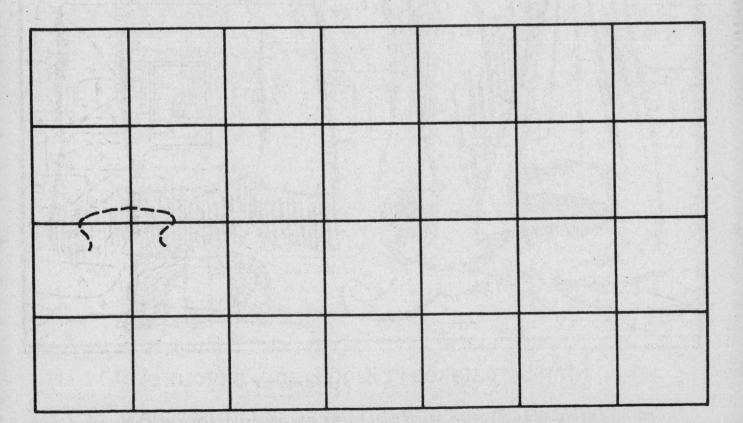

Find 6 mistakes in King Henry's picture.

Answers: The light switch is on the tablecloth; the horizon outside the window is upside-down; one shoe is missing; a doorknob is on the belt buckle; fish and scissors are in the punch; half a mustache is on the king.

Find the twin candles.

Answer: 1 and 6

FOLLOW THE DOTS and see what happened to Santa when he took a rest in Hawaii.

COLOR BY NUMBER:

"I came up for my bannock cake too!"

1-green 2-red 3-orange 4-light blue 5-white 6-pink

Carol singing has been popular since the Middle Ages.

"God rest ye merry gentlemen . . . ."

People in many lands believe that an elf watches over children during the Christmas season.

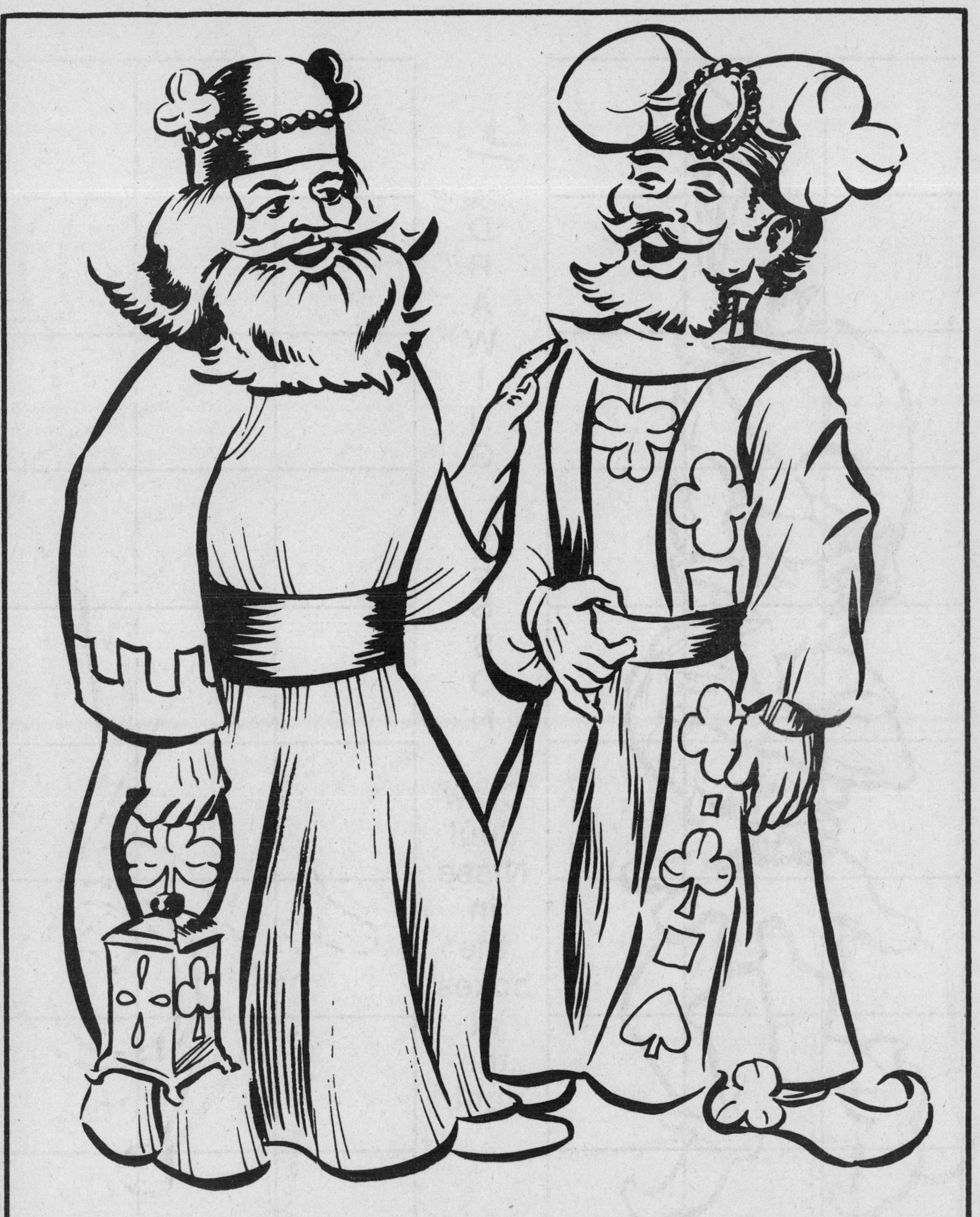

How many hidden shamrocks can you find?

Answer: 7

DRAWING LESSON

Draw Júúl Nisse in the boxes at the right.

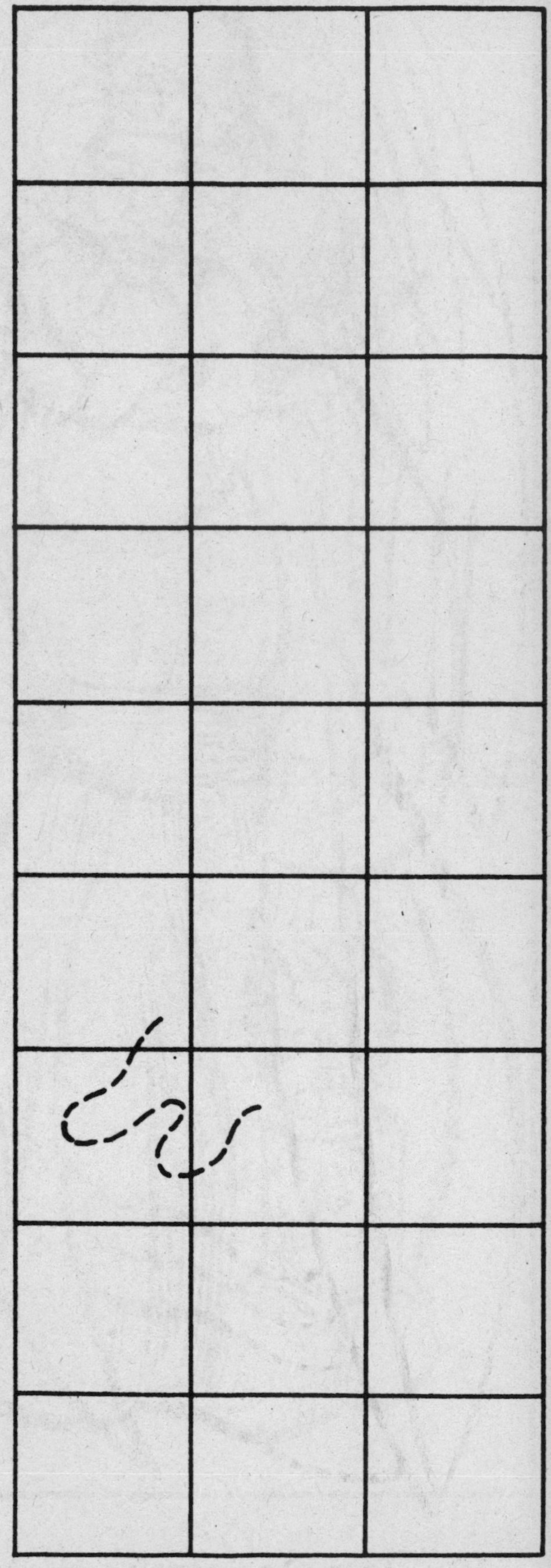

Santa's Christmas wish to all people around the world —
"Peace on Earth!"

FOLLOW THE DOTS and see
who is playing a Christmas trick.

Lead the Good Elf to his correct page in the elves' book of lists.

How many hidden hearts can you find?

Answer: 8

Lead each of the Three Wise Men to the manger.

FOLLOW THE DOTS and see
why Santa can't find the chimney.